Standard Grade
Biology
revision notes

Text © 1998 Denyse Kozub
Design and layout © 1998 Leckie & Leckie Ltd
Cover image © Photodisc/Getty Images

4th edition (reprinted 2006)

ISBN 1-898890-86-2

Published by
Leckie & Leckie Ltd, 3rd floor, 4 Queen Street, Edinburgh, EH2 1JF
Tel: 0131 220 6831 Fax: 0131 225 9987
enquiries@leckieandleckie.co.uk   www.leckieandleckie.co.uk

Edited by
Andrew Morton

Special thanks to
Alison Irving (proofreading) and Caleb Rutherford (cover design)

A CIP Catalogue record for this book is available from the British Library.

Leckie & Leckie is a division of Granada Learning Limited.

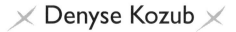

Denyse Kozub

CONTENTS

These Revision Notes cover all the Knowledge and Understanding for General and Credit level at Standard Grade. Your teacher will be able to tell you which parts you need to cover if you are sitting the General level paper only.

In the text, key words are printed in **bold type**.

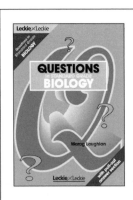

To test your Knowledge and Understanding of Standard Grade Biology, we recommend that you obtain a copy of Leckie & Leckie's other Standard Grade Biology book, *Questions in Standard Grade Biology*, from your school, college or bookshop.

UNIT ONE: The Biosphere

INVESTIGATING AN ECOSYSTEM

The place where an organism (i.e. an animal or plant) lives is called a **habitat**. If we want to find out as much as possible about a particular habitat, we have to carry out an investigation which involves

1. collecting the organisms   2. identifying the organisms   3. measuring the physical conditions

1. Sampling techniques

Obviously we cannot collect all the organisms within a habitat, so we must take a sample. Two examples of sampling techniques are:

For animals – a pitfall trap	For plants – a quadrat
The cup is placed in the hole, making sure that the top is level with the ground so that the animals fall in. However, some animals which fall in may be eaten by predators, such as spiders, which also fall in. A lid is often placed over the cup to keep out rain and larger predators.	A quadrat is a square frame used to mark an area. The one shown is divided into smaller squares. It is thrown **randomly** on the area being sampled. The number of squares which contain the plant being studied are counted, not the number of plants in each square. The more samples taken, the more reliable the result.

2. Identifying organisms

To identify organisms in a sample a **key** can be used.

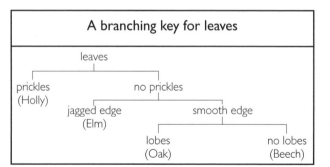

A branching key for leaves
leaves
prickles (Holly) — no prickles
jagged edge (Elm) — smooth edge
lobes (Oak) — no lobes (Beech)

A paired statement key for leaves
1. with prickles...Holly
with no prickles...2
2. jagged edge...Elm
smooth edge...3
3. lobes...Oak
no lobes..Beech

3. Measuring abiotic factors

An **abiotic** factor is a **physical** factor (e.g. **light** or **moisture**) which can affect the organisms living in a particular habitat. Examples of other abiotic factors are **temperature** and **oxygen concentration**. An abiotic factor can normally be measured using a meter.

Measuring light	Measuring moisture
A light meter is used. To avoid errors, you must be careful not to shade the meter and always hold it the same way when making the reading.	A moisture meter is used. To avoid errors, you must be careful that you place the moisture probe firmly in the ground and wipe it afterwards.

Effect of abiotic factors	Reason why
green plants not found in areas with low light intensity	plants need light for photosynthesis
most land organisms not found in very cold areas	enzymes do not work well at low temperatures and water is often frozen

HOW IT WORKS

1. What is an ecosystem?

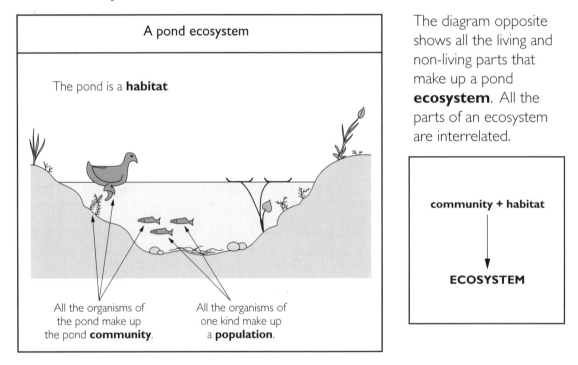

The diagram opposite shows all the living and non-living parts that make up a pond **ecosystem**. All the parts of an ecosystem are interrelated.

community + habitat

↓

ECOSYSTEM

2. Food and energy in an ecosystem

All living things need energy. They obtain their energy from food. All the energy in an ecosystem comes from the sun, because plants use light energy from the sun to make food.

Plants are called **producers** because they make their own food by a process called **photosynthesis**.

Animals are called **consumers** because they obtain their energy by eating plants or other animals.

The way in which energy, in the form of food, passes from plants to animals and then to other animals can be shown by a **food chain**.

grass ⟶ field vole ⟶ kestrel

| **This is a producer.** | **This is a primary consumer.** | **This is a secondary consumer.** |

The **arrow** in a food chain points from the food to the feeder and shows the **direction of energy flow**.

3. Food webs

A plant or animal usually belongs to several food chains. This connection between food chains forms a **food web**.

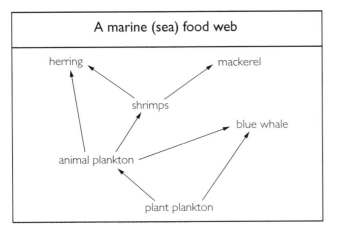

A marine (sea) food web

herring
mackerel
shrimps
blue whale
animal plankton
plant plankton

All food webs are delicately balanced. The removal of one organism can have a serious effect on the food web.

In the marine (sea) food web shown opposite, if fishermen catch large numbers of shrimps then the numbers of herring and mackerel might fall because they have less food.

4. Energy loss in a food chain

As energy is passed along a food chain, each organism uses some of it. This means that energy is lost at each stage in a food chain. The ways in which energy is lost are shown below.

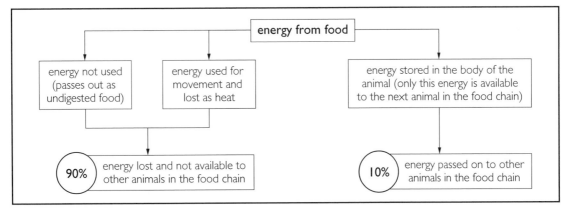

energy from food

energy not used (passes out as undigested food)

energy used for movement and lost as heat

energy stored in the body of the animal (only this energy is available to the next animal in the food chain)

90% energy lost and not available to other animals in the food chain

10% energy passed on to other animals in the food chain

5. Pyramid of numbers

As you move along a food chain, very often the size of the organism increases but the number of organisms decreases.

plant plankton ⟶ animal plankton ⟶ herring

(very large numbers of small organisms) (fewer, larger organisms) (few, even larger organisms)

This can be shown by drawing a pyramid.

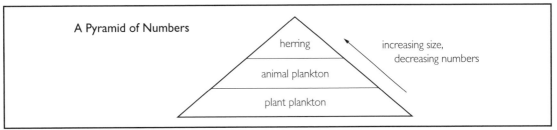

A Pyramid of Numbers

herring
animal plankton
plant plankton

increasing size, decreasing numbers

A more accurate idea of the quantity of animal and plant material in a food chain is obtained by constructing **a pyramid of biomass**. This represents the mass of all the organisms at each level and gives a much better representation of the actual quantity of animal and plant material at each level.

6. Population growth

The size of most populations tends to stay roughly the same. The size of a population stays the same as long as the birth rate is the same as the death rate.

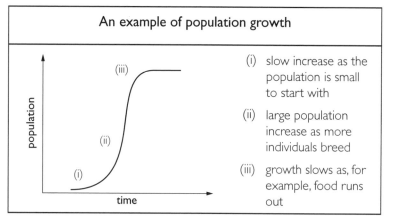

An example of population growth
(i) slow increase as the population is small to start with
(ii) large population increase as more individuals breed
(iii) growth slows as, for example, food runs out

Eventually population growth is checked by some or all of the following:

(a) predators
(b) disease
(c) limited food supply
(d) lack of space which may prevent breeding

7. Competition

Plants compete for light and water. Animals compete for food and a place to live. If different animals eat the same food then competition is more intense. When competition occurs, some organisms will be more successful than others. These organisms will be more likely to survive.

8. Nutrient cycles

Bacteria and fungi are very important to animals and plants. They feed on dead animals and plants and are known as **decomposers**.

Decomposers are important because:
(a) they get rid of dead animals and plants
(b) they release chemicals from dead organisms which go into the soil and help keep it fertile.

9. The nitrogen cycle

All living things need **nitrogen** to make **protein**. Plants obtain nitrogen from the soil by taking in nitrates. Animals obtain nitrogen by eating plants or other animals.

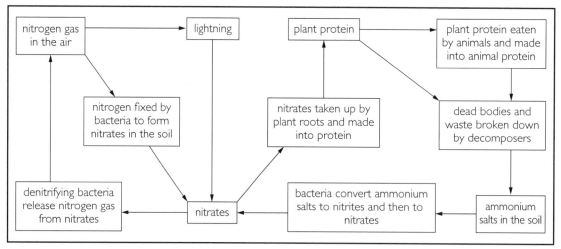

Nitrogen fixing means absorbing nitrogen gas from the atmosphere to make **nitrates**. Some bacteria in the soil can do this. Also, some plants (e.g. peas and clover) have swellings (nodules) on their roots in which these types of bacteria live.

CONTROL AND MANAGEMENT

1. Sources of pollution

Pollution is caused by the presence of a substance (e.g. oil in the sea) that is harmful to an animal or plant. Pollutants come from three main sources – **industry**, **agriculture** and **the home**. They can affect air, fresh water, sea and land. Here are some examples:

Source of pollution	Substance which causes pollution	Effect of pollutant
industry	sulphur dioxide	causes acid rain
agriculture	pesticides	can be washed into rivers and poison organisms
the home	car exhaust fumes	the particles in car exhausts can result in breathing difficulties

2. Controlling pollution

It is essential that the activities of people are controlled so that pollution is reduced, for example:

Pollutant	Method of control
soot in smoke	Clean Air Acts prohibit factories from releasing black smoke
lead in exhaust fumes	introduction of unleaded petrol
domestic sewage	treatment at sewage works before waste is discharged

3. Sewage and pollution

Sewage is a common pollutant. Waste like this is called **organic waste** and can cause many changes in the water. Organic waste provides food for bacteria and allows them to grow and reproduce. When bacteria feed on the sewage, they use up the oxygen in the water. This means that there is less oxygen for other organisms such as fish and insects.

The chart below shows the changes that take place in a stretch of river polluted by sewage.

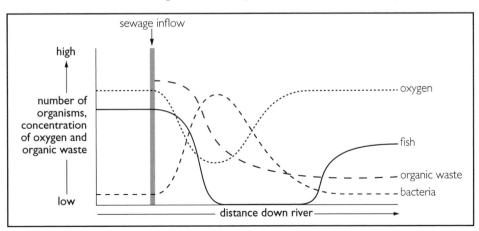

As the concentration of sewage pollution rises, the population of bacteria rises because the bacteria feed off the sewage which provides raw materials and energy for growth and reproduction.

At the same time, the concentration of oxygen falls because the bacteria use up the oxygen as they break down the organic waste in the sewage.

Consequently, animals, such as fish, stonefly nymphs and shrimps, decrease in numbers.

4. Pollution indicators

Some animals are only able to live in water which contains a lot of oxygen. Other animals can survive in water that contains little or no oxygen. The presence or absence of particular organisms can indicate whether the water is polluted or not. These animals are called **indicator species**.

Animals found in water with low levels of oxygen	sludge worm	rat-tailed maggot	blood worm

Animals found in water with high levels of oxygen	mayfly nymph	stonefly nymph	shrimp

5. Energy sources and pollution

Most of our energy comes from power stations which burn **fossil fuels** (coal, oil and gas).

This results in harmful gases, such as sulphur dioxide and nitrogen dioxide, being released into the air. When these gases dissolve in rain water they form acid rain.

Some **renewable** alternatives to fossil fuels as sources of energy are:

(a) solar power (using the sun's light energy)
(b) wind power (using the movement energy from wind)
(c) tidal power (using the movement energy of tides)
(d) **nuclear power** is also an alternative but it can be dangerous because it produces radioactive waste which can cause cancer and is difficult to get rid of.

6. Management of resources

People have obtained many resources from the Earth (coal, oil, timber, food, etc.). This has resulted in the destruction or disruption of many habitats. Conservation is very important because many resources will not last forever or may run short. Three examples of poor management of resources and some possible solutions are:

Poor management	Possible solution
overfishing in the North Sea	have fish quotas, or increase net mesh size to allow smaller fish to survive
destruction of rain forests	produce food more efficiently and control the areas being cut down for agriculture
overuse of land, leading to desert soils	use different agricultural practices (crop rotation, natural fertilisers)

UNIT TWO: The World of Plants

INTRODUCING PLANTS

The sun is the source of all energy on Earth. Plants are the link between the sun and other living things. Without green plants practically all life on Earth would not exist. People rely on there being a wide variety of plants, yet plant habitats are under constant threat.

1. The importance of plants

Plants are required:

(a) for plant breeding to produce new varieties
(b) as habitats for other organisms
(c) as the initial source of food in a food web
(d) for gas balance in the atmosphere
(e) for raw materials, food and medicines
(f) for improving the appearance of our surroundings

2. The uses of plants

The range of use of plants is enormous. They can be used for food, raw materials in industry and also for medicines. Here are some examples:

Foods	Raw materials	Medicines
– wheat for bread – palms for oil – sugar cane for sugar – grapes for wine	– jute plant for string – flax plant for linen – rose petals for perfume – heather for dyes	– foxglove plant for digitalis (a muscle relaxant) – poppy for morphine – cinchona tree for quinine

3. The effects of reducing plant species

Plants, especially trees, are essential for maintaining life on this planet. However, certain human activities are having quite serious effects on the environment. The destruction of habitats (such as the rainforests) means that many species are being lost. Other examples are:

(a) destruction of the eucalyptus trees in Australia has resulted in a decrease in the koala population because this tree is their main food source
(b) selective breeding has resulted in a loss of certain plant species.

4. The potential uses of plants

Some new techniques have allowed scientists to use plants to produce new products or to grow greater numbers of the plant, for example:

(a) the extraction of protein (mycoprotein) from a fungus which can then be used as a food;
(b) the growing (culture) of oil palm cells to produce large numbers of individual plants from which palm oil can be extracted.

Scientists are always looking for plants that they can use to produce new products. There are still many species of plants which have not yet been discovered and may have a potential use. The destruction of habitats, however, means that some of these plants may be lost forever.

The potential to use different vegetable oils as fuels is one new use of plants which is being investigated. However, investigations such as this can take a very long time and be expensive.

GROWING PLANTS

In order to reproduce, some plants produce **seeds**. This involves a number of stages in the plant life cycle.

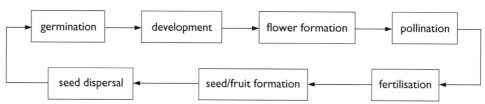

1. Seed structure and germination

Germination is the development of a new plant from the embryo plant in a seed. Seeds need **water**, **oxygen** and the **right temperature** before they will germinate.

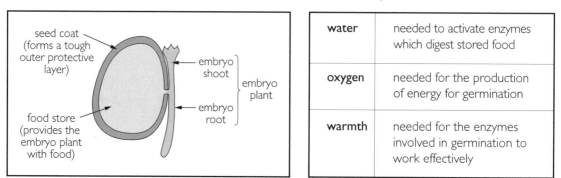

water	needed to activate enzymes which digest stored food
oxygen	needed for the production of energy for germination
warmth	needed for the enzymes involved in germination to work effectively

At very high (above 45°C) and very low (below 5°C) temperatures seed germination is often poor. Seeds normally have a high percentage germination over a range of temperatures from around 15°C to 30°C. The temperature at which germination is most successful for a species of plant is known as the optimum temperature.

2. Structure of a flower

To reproduce sexually, some plants produce flowers. The flowers contain the sex organs.

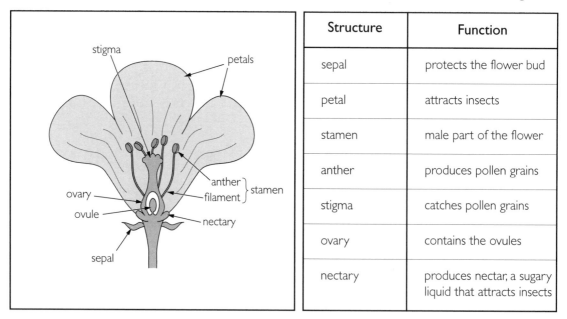

Structure	Function
sepal	protects the flower bud
petal	attracts insects
stamen	male part of the flower
anther	produces pollen grains
stigma	catches pollen grains
ovary	contains the ovules
nectary	produces nectar, a sugary liquid that attracts insects

3. Pollination

A new seed will be formed when the male sex cell in a pollen grain joins up with a female sex cell. Sex cells are called **gametes**.

Pollination involves the transfer of pollen from the anther to the stigma.

Many plants are pollinated by insects or by the wind.

	Insect-pollinated flowers	Wind-pollinated flowers
petals	brightly coloured and scented to attract insects	small, dull petals, as there is no need to attract insects
pollen	sticky or spiky to stick to insects' bodies	large numbers of very light pollen grains that will be carried by the wind
stigmas	sticky so that when insects brush past the pollen sticks to the stigma	feathery stigmas hang outside the flower so that pollen can be trapped on them
stamens	inside the flower so that insects will brush past them and pick up pollen	large stamens dangle outside the flower to catch the wind which blows away the pollen
nectar	sticky sweet substance that attracts insects	none produced as there is no need to attract insects

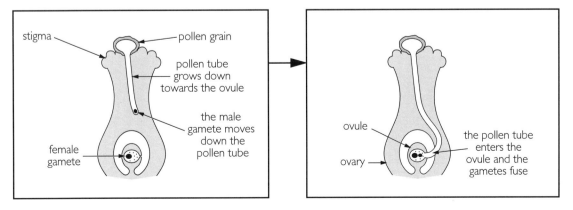

(flowers not drawn to scale)

4. Fertilisation

After the pollen grain has landed on the stigma, a tube grows down from the pollen grain to the ovule. The male gamete travels down the tube and fuses with the female gamete. This fusion process is called **fertilisation**. Once fertilisation has taken place, the **ovule** becomes the **seed** and the **ovary** becomes a **fruit**. The petals then die and drop off.

5. Seed dispersal

The seeds are contained in the fruit. There are different kinds of fruit, for example:

(a) Fleshy fruits (e.g. tomato, plum, apple). Here the main part of the fruit is soft and juicy.
(b) Dry fruits (e.g. dandelion, sycamore). Here the main part of the fruit is hard and dry.

Seeds must be carried away from the parent plant to reduce overcrowding and competition for water, light and minerals.

Seeds can be dispersed in different ways, for example:

Dispersal method	Description of some examples	Seeds/fruits
wind	– may have extensions which act as parachutes or wings to carry the seed in the wind (e.g. dandelion and sycamore) – fruits may also be shaken like a pepper pot (e.g. poppy)	
animal (external)	– carried away by animals and dropped (e.g. hazelnuts) – have hooks which attach to the animal's fur and may be rubbed off later (e.g. burdock)	
animal (internal)	– brightly coloured to attract animals. When eaten, the seed (e.g. cherry, tomato) survives digestive juices and is passed out in the faeces	

6. Asexual reproduction

Sexual reproduction involves two parents. Many flowering plants can reproduce in a way that involves only one parent. This is called **asexual reproduction** and does not involve the formation of sex cells.

There are many ways in which plants can reproduce asexually but three examples are:

Runners	Tubers	Bulbs
A runner is a side shoot which grows out from the parent. Where it touches the ground a new plant grows (e.g. strawberry, spider plant).	An underground food store. Food made in the leaves is stored in the tuber and used as an energy source for new growth (e.g. potato, dahlia).	A bulb has thick fleshy leaves full of stored food which is used for the growth of a new plant the following year (e.g. daffodils, onions).

7. Advantages of asexual reproduction

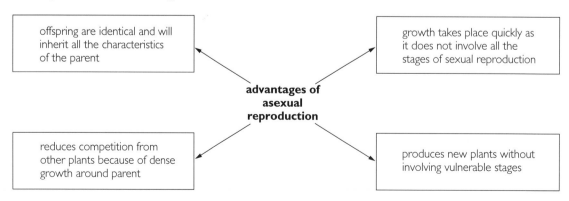

offspring are identical and will inherit all the characteristics of the parent

growth takes place quickly as it does not involve all the stages of sexual reproduction

advantages of asexual reproduction

reduces competition from other plants because of dense growth around parent

produces new plants without involving vulnerable stages

8. Comparing asexual and sexual reproduction

	Asexual reproduction	Sexual reproduction
Advantages	– early quick growth is possible because there are no vulnerable stages involved – offspring will all have the parent plant's good characteristics	– variation takes place which may be an advantage if conditions change – allows dispersal of seeds to new areas
Disadvantages	– because there is no variation, weak characteristics can be passed on – competition may be reduced, but overcrowding can take place	– involves many vulnerable stages which the young plant may not survive

Asexual reproduction involves the formation of **clones**. A clone is a group of cells or organisms all originating from the same parent and all genetically identical to each other and the parent.

9. Artificial propagation

Gardeners make use of a plant's ability to reproduce asexually by using different methods of propagation. Instead of growing seeds, they take a small section of stem, root or leaf. Under the right conditions, these will grow into a whole plant identical to the parent plant.

Three common methods of propagation are:

Cuttings	Grafting	Layering
Cuttings are small pieces of stem cut from a healthy plant. The cut stem can be placed in a rooting medium to encourage root growth (e.g. geranium).	A portion of the plant with good flower or fruit growth is taken and joined to a plant with an established strong root system (e.g. roses and fruit bushes).	The stem of the parent plant is bent until it touches the ground. It is then held in place until roots have formed (e.g. carnations).

10. Commercial advantages of artificial propagation

The ability of plants to carry out asexual reproduction has brought enormous benefits in both agriculture and horticulture.

(a) It is a quick method of producing large numbers of genetically identical new plants.
(b) Particular varieties that are required can be produced easily.
(c) Techniques such as grafting produce a plant that will grow fruit or flowers of a known variety or quality.

MAKING FOOD

1. How plants make food

Plants make food by a process called **photosynthesis**.

Plants use light energy to make food from carbon dioxide and water. The chemical **chlorophyll** (which gives plants their green colour) traps the light energy from the sun. This light energy is then converted to chemical energy in the form of glucose. All food chains and food webs rely on plants to manufacture food at the start of the food chain.

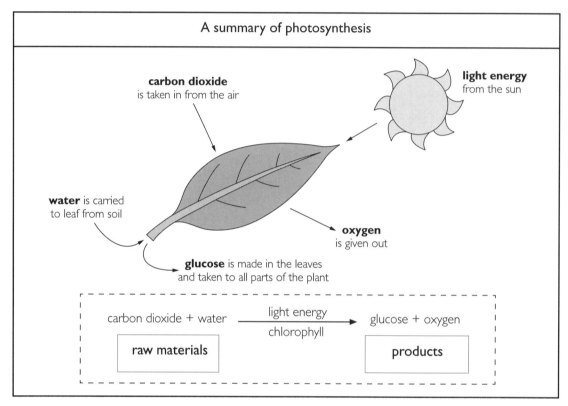

A summary of photosynthesis

carbon dioxide is taken in from the air

light energy from the sun

water is carried to leaf from soil

oxygen is given out

glucose is made in the leaves and taken to all parts of the plant

carbon dioxide + water $\xrightarrow[\text{chlorophyll}]{\text{light energy}}$ glucose + oxygen

raw materials   **products**

During photosynthesis, carbon dioxide diffuses into leaves through tiny pores called **stomata** (singular – **stoma**). At the same time, oxygen and water vapour diffuse out of leaves through the stomata. At night, when plants are not photosynthesising, the stomata close to reduce water loss.

2. The use of glucose by plants

The glucose manufactured during photosynthesis is used by plants in a number of ways.

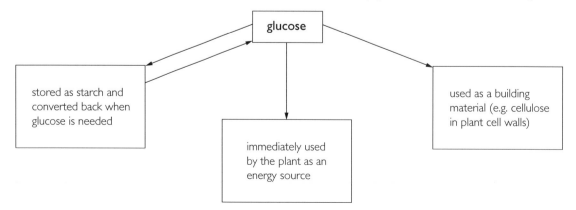

glucose

stored as starch and converted back when glucose is needed

immediately used by the plant as an energy source

used as a building material (e.g. cellulose in plant cell walls)

3. Transport in a plant

Xylem carries water and minerals from the soil to the leaves for photosynthesis.

Phloem carries sugars from the leaves to every part of the plant.

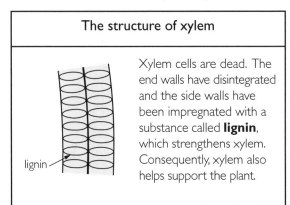

The structure of xylem

Xylem cells are dead. The end walls have disintegrated and the side walls have been impregnated with a substance called **lignin**, which strengthens xylem. Consequently, xylem also helps support the plant.

lignin

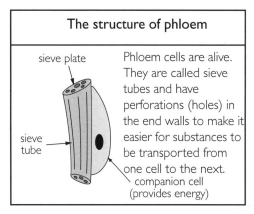

The structure of phloem

Phloem cells are alive. They are called sieve tubes and have perforations (holes) in the end walls to make it easier for substances to be transported from one cell to the next.

sieve plate

sieve tube

companion cell (provides energy)

4. Structure of a leaf

A leaf has a large surface area and is very thin because:

(a) A large surface allows maximum exposure to sunlight.

(b) A thin leaf means that gases can diffuse quickly to and from the photosynthesising leaf cells.

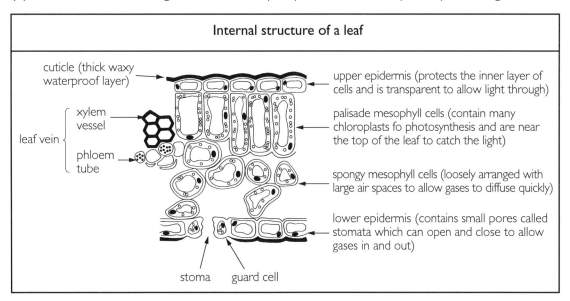

Internal structure of a leaf

cuticle (thick waxy waterproof layer)

leaf vein
- xylem vessel
- phloem tube

stoma   guard cell

upper epidermis (protects the inner layer of cells and is transparent to allow light through)

palisade mesophyll cells (contain many chloroplasts fo photosynthesis and are near the top of the leaf to catch the light)

spongy mesophyll cells (loosely arranged with large air spaces to allow gases to diffuse quickly)

lower epidermis (contains small pores called stomata which can open and close to allow gases in and out)

5. Limiting factors

Photosynthesis depends on the availability of light and carbon dioxide and on a suitable temperature. If any one of these factors is in short supply, it will limit the rate of photosynthesis. Light, carbon dioxide and temperature therefore act as limiting factors.

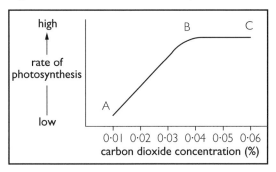

high

rate of photosynthesis

low

A

B   C

0·01 0·02 0·03 0·04 0·05 0·06
carbon dioxide concentration (%)

In the graph, carbon dioxide concentration is increased. Temperature and light are kept constant. The limiting factor between A and B is the carbon dioxide concentration. The limiting factor between B and C is either light or temperature.

The rate of photosynthesis will only increase further if the limiting factor is increased.

UNIT 3: Animal Survival

THE NEED FOR FOOD

1. Why we need food

All living things need food as a source of raw materials for growth and as a source of energy. There are two ways in which organisms obtain their food:

(a) Plants make their own food by the process of photosynthesis.

(b) Animals rely on ready-made food, either by eating plants or other animals.

Any food contains a mixture of chemicals. The main ones are:

Chemical	Function
carbohydrates (e.g. sugar and starch)	provide energy
proteins	needed for growth and repair
fats	provide energy and help insulate the body
vitamins and minerals (e.g. vitamin C and calcium)	needed to help enzyme action

2. Chemical structure of food types

Carbohydrates, fats and proteins are mostly large molecules formed from many similar, smaller molecules linked together.

	Carbohydrate	Fat	Protein
elements present	carbon (C) hydrogen (H) oxygen (O)	carbon hydrogen oxygen	carbon hydrogen oxygen nitrogen (N)
basic units they are built from	sugar molecules	fatty acids and glycerol	amino acids
diagram of structure	glucose molecules in a chain to form e.g. starch or cellulose	glycerol, fatty acids	amino acids in a chain to form a protein

3. Breaking down food

Much of the food we eat must be changed before the body can use it. This involves the breakdown of large insoluble food particles into smaller soluble particles that can pass from the small intestine into the bloodstream.

The breakdown of food takes place in two steps:

(a) the **mechanical breakdown** by **teeth**
(b) the **chemical breakdown** by **enzymes** e.g.   starch $\xrightarrow{\text{enzymes}}$ glucose
                                                                    (insoluble)   (soluble)

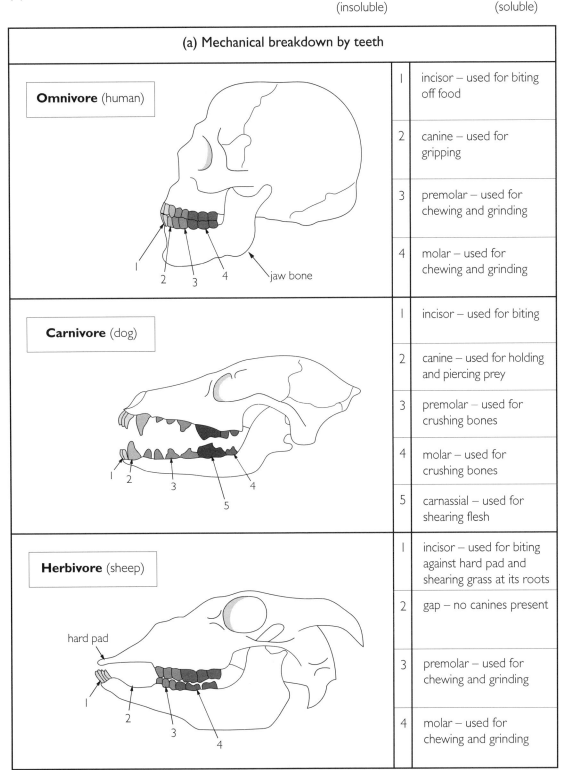

(a) Mechanical breakdown by teeth		
Omnivore (human)	I	incisor – used for biting off food
	2	canine – used for gripping
	3	premolar – used for chewing and grinding
	4	molar – used for chewing and grinding
Carnivore (dog)	I	incisor – used for biting
	2	canine – used for holding and piercing prey
	3	premolar – used for crushing bones
	4	molar – used for crushing bones
	5	carnassial – used for shearing flesh
Herbivore (sheep)	I	incisor – used for biting against hard pad and shearing grass at its roots
	2	gap – no canines present
	3	premolar – used for chewing and grinding
	4	molar – used for chewing and grinding

(b) The chemical breakdown of food takes place in the **alimentary canal** (**gut**).

The adult human gut is about five metres long and is coiled round to fit into the body. Each part of the gut has a different job to do. The movement of food from the mouth to the anus is slow and may take up to two days.

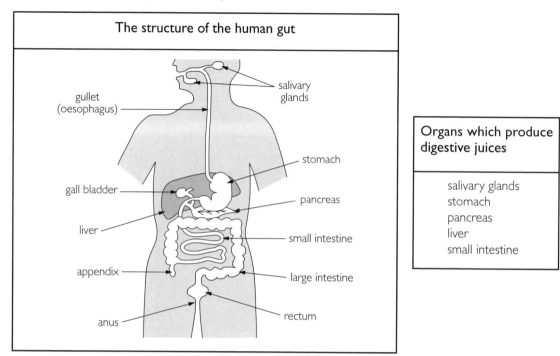

4. Moving food along the gut

Food cannot move along the gut by itself – it has to be pushed. This is done by muscles in the gut wall. When food moves along the gut, muscles in the wall contract behind the food and relax in front of it. This pushes the food along the gut. This action by the muscles is called **peristalsis**.

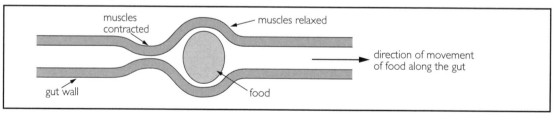

5. How food is digested

As food passes along the gut, digestive juices are produced by various organs. These digestive juices contain enzymes which digest (break down) the carbohydrates, fats and proteins in the food.

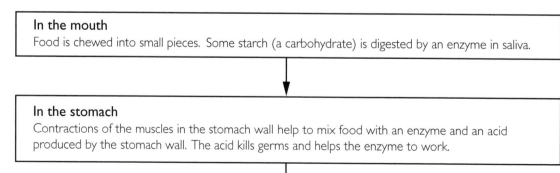

In the mouth
Food is chewed into small pieces. Some starch (a carbohydrate) is digested by an enzyme in saliva.

In the stomach
Contractions of the muscles in the stomach wall help to mix food with an enzyme and an acid produced by the stomach wall. The acid kills germs and helps the enzyme to work.

In the small intestine

All digestion is completed by more enzymes produced by the small intestine and the pancreas.

Food is now in a form the body can use and it is absorbed through the wall of the intestine into the bloodstream, which carries it to the liver.

The small intestine is able to carry out this job efficiently because:

    (a)   it is long and folded to create a bigger surface;

    (b)   the surface is increased by tiny finger-like projections called **villi**;

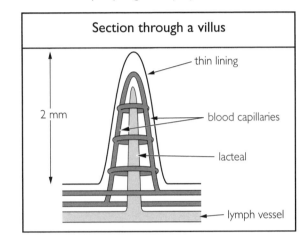

Section through a villus

2 mm — thin lining — blood capillaries — lacteal — lymph vessel

    (c)   the wall is very thin to allow digested food through quickly and easily;

    (d)   the wall has a good blood supply to carry the digested food away

          – glucose and amino acids pass into the bloodstream;

          – fatty acids and glycerol pass into the **lacteal**.

In the large intestine

What passes into the large intestine is a very watery mash, because it still contains a lot of water. Most of this water is absorbed back into the blood and the undigested remains (faeces) are stored in the rectum and eventually pass out through the anus.

6. Digestive enzymes

Digestive enzymes change the food you eat by breaking down the large, insoluble food molecules into smaller soluble food molecules that can easily be absorbed into the bloodstream. Each type of food needs a different enzyme to break it down. (See page 28.)

Enzyme group	Substrate	Product	Example of enzyme in this group and the organ which produces it
amylase	starch	maltose	salivary amylase – salivary glands
protease	protein	amino acids	pepsin – stomach
lipase	fats & oils	fatty acids & glycerol	pancreatic lipase – pancreas

REPRODUCTION IN ANIMALS

1. Types of reproduction

There are two ways reproduction can take place:

(a) **Asexual reproduction**: there is only one parent. It does not involve the formation and fusion of sex cells, e.g. amoeba, sea anemone.

(b) **Sexual reproduction**: this type of reproduction involves two parents. The parents have sex organs which produce sex cells. The sex cells are called **gametes**. The male gametes are **sperm**, the female gametes are **eggs**.

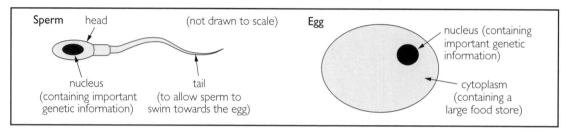

2. Fertilisation and development

For sexual reproduction to take place a sperm nucleus must fuse with an egg nucleus. This is called fertilisation. There are two types of fertilisation:

(a) **External fertilisation**: the eggs are released from the body into the external surroundings and the male then sheds his sperm over the eggs (e.g. fish).

(b) **Internal fertilisation**: the eggs are fertilised by the sperm inside the female's body (e.g. mammals). This is important to land-living animals, as there is no water outside the body to carry the sperm to the egg.

3. Human reproduction

Human reproduction begins with sexual intercourse. During sexual intercourse millions of sperm are passed into the woman's vagina. The sperm then swim up through the uterus and into the oviduct. The sperm are attracted to chemicals produced by the egg which has been released into the oviduct.

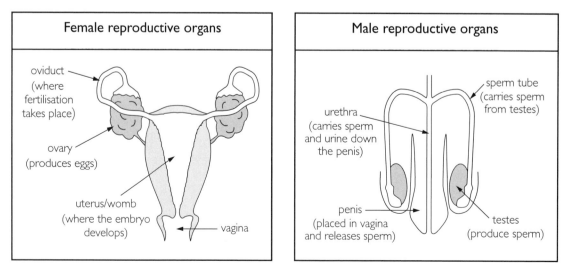

4. Human development

When the sperm meet an egg, they group round it and the head of one sperm will enter the egg. The nuclei of the sperm and the egg join together. The membrane round the egg then stops any other sperm from entering. The fertilised egg now continues down the oviduct to the uterus, dividing many times. The ball of cells, the embryo, attaches itself to the wall of the uterus and begins to develop.

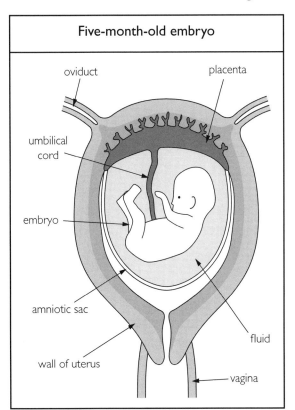

Five-month-old embryo

The embryo develops in a bag-like structure called the **amniotic sac**. This is filled with fluid which helps to protect the embryo as it grows. The fluid cushions it against any bumps or knocks.

The growing embryo is attached to the uterus wall by the umbilical cord. The umbilical cord passes into the **placenta** which is attached to the wall of the uterus. The umbilical cord carries carbon dioxide and waste from the baby to the placenta and oxygen and food to the baby.

The mother's blood does not mix with that of the baby, but the blood vessels are very close and materials can pass easily from the mother to the baby and vice versa. Poisonous substances (such as nicotine, alcohol and drugs) can also pass into the baby's blood system and cause harm.

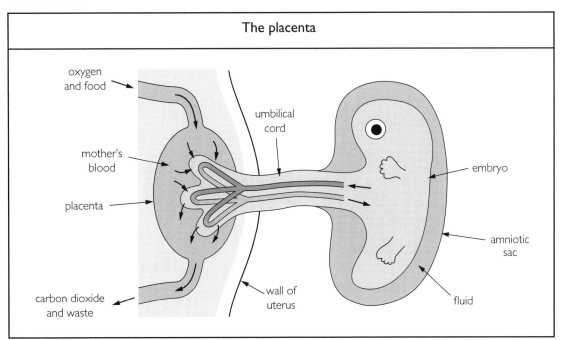

The placenta

After birth, the young of mammals are very dependent on the adults for care and protection. This is unlike many other animals (e.g. the frog or trout) where the adults have nothing more to do with development after the eggs are fertilised.

5. Trout development

Trouts' eggs and sperm are shed into water. The water stops the eggs from drying out and also allows the sperm to swim to the eggs.

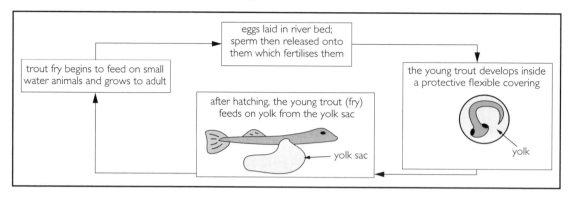

6. Egg numbers and survival chances

Many sex cells and young are destroyed during the various stages of development by, for example:

(a) eggs not being fertilised   (b) eggs being eaten   (c) eggs being diseased

The greater the risks involved in the type of reproduction, the greater the number of eggs produced.

Animal	Number of eggs produced per season
herring	5,000,000
turtle	100

As the survival chances of the herring are very low (because fertilisation and development are external), the herring produces very large numbers of eggs to compensate and ensure that at least a small proportion will survive and become adults.

WATER AND WASTE

The kidneys are important because they help to get rid of poisonous waste and regulate the volume of water in the body.

1. Structure of the kidneys

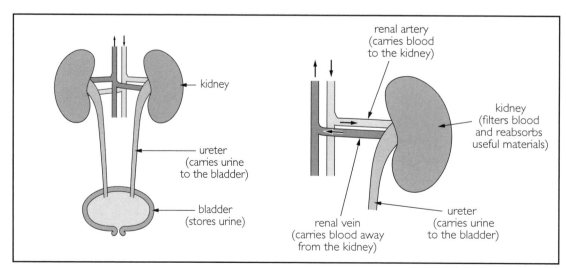

2. The kidneys and water balance

Our bodies are 60% water. Too much or too little water is dangerous. We can gain water or lose water in different ways, but the volume of water we gain must be equal to the volume of water we lose. This is called water balance. The kidneys help to maintain this balance by producing more or less urine depending on the body's intake.

How water enters and leaves the body			
daily water gain	cm³	daily water loss	cm³
food	750	urine	1500
drink	1500	sweat	300
water made during respiration*	250	breathing	600
		faeces	100
TOTAL	2500	TOTAL	2500

* glucose + oxygen ⟶ carbon dioxide + **water** + energy (see page 30)

3. How urea is produced

During digestion, proteins in our food are broken down by enzymes into amino acids. These amino acids are carried to the liver to be built into new proteins. Any extra amino acids not used are broken down by the liver into **urea** which is a poisonous substance. The urea is then taken to the kidneys where it is removed in the urine.

4. The kidneys and waste

As well as removing urea from the blood, the kidneys also filter out other poisonous substances. All our blood is filtered by the kidneys about 300 times a day. The filtering is carried out by millions of tiny structures called **nephrons**.

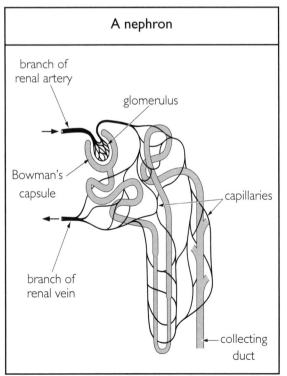

A nephron

Blood enters a nephron along a branch of the **renal artery**. The branch divides into a bundle of capillaries called a **glomerulus**. The glomerulus sits in a cup-shaped structure called the **Bowman's capsule**. The blood is filtered from the glomerulus into the Bowman's capsule. As the filtrate moves along the tubules of the nephron, useful substances such as glucose, amino acids and much of the water are reabsorbed back into the blood. The remaining liquid is called urine and contains water, urea and some salts. The urine is carried by the **collecting ducts** to the **ureter** and then on to the **bladder** where it is stored until it leaves the body.

5. Control of water balance

No matter how much water the body gains or loses, the kidneys adjust the volume of urine produced to help maintain water balance. This process is controlled by a chemical produced in the brain called **antidiuretic hormone** (ADH).

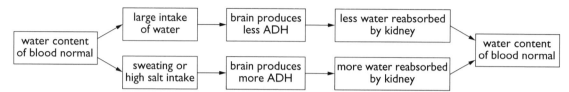

6. Kidney damage

If the kidneys stop working because of disease or damage, then the person will die. Kidney failure can be treated by using **kidney machines** or by **kidney transplants**. A person can be put on a kidney machine right away if they are in danger, but may have to wait a long time for a donor kidney. However, kidney machines are very expensive and involve the patient spending a lot of time connected to them.

Kidney transplants are not frequent because of a shortage of donors. The transplanted kidney can also be rejected by the body of the patient.

RESPONDING TO THE ENVIRONMENT

The environment is anything which influences the life of an animal or a plant. It can be, for example, the presence of other organisms, the climate or, in the case of animals, the quality and quantity of food.

1. Responses to changes in the environment

The way in which an animal responds to a stimulus from its surroundings is important to the animal's survival. The conditions an animal chooses are the best for its survival.

Animal	Stimulus	Response	Importance to animal
woodlouse	moisture	moves about more slowly	ensures woodlouse stays in a moist environment (it needs moisture to breathe)
blowfly maggots	light	move away from light	ensures maggots stay in dark places to obtain food and protection (e.g. in dead animals)

2. Rhythmical behaviour

Some environmental conditions change regularly (e.g. hours of daylight and daily temperatures). Many animals change their behaviour in response to these regular changes in the environment. These changes are examples of rhythmical behaviour. The stimulus that sets off the change is called a **trigger stimulus**.

Animal	Rhythmical behaviour pattern	Trigger stimulus	Importance to animal
squirrel	hibernation	decreasing day length and temperature	conserves energy when food is in short supply

UNIT FOUR: Investigating Cells

INVESTIGATING LIVING CELLS

Cells are the basic units of all living things (organisms).

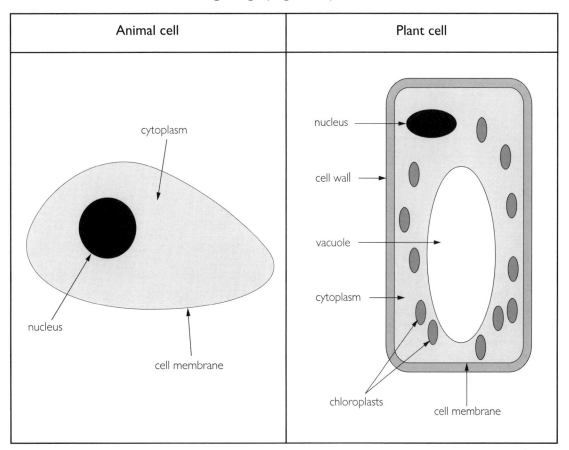

Animal cell	Plant cell

Stains are used in the preparation of microscope slides to make cell structures (such as the nucleus, cytoplasm and cell membrane) more clearly visible.

INVESTIGATING DIFFUSION

Diffusion is the movement of molecules from an area of high concentration to an area of low concentration until they are evenly spread.

1. Diffusion and living cells

Some substances can get into and out of a cell by diffusion through the cell membrane. Examples of substances that diffuse into or out of a cell are shown below.

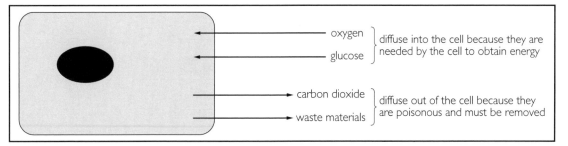

2. Diffusion through cell membranes

The cell membrane does not allow all molecules to pass through it. Some molecules are too large to pass through (e.g. starch).

Potatoes are made up of many living cells. Each cell is surrounded by a membrane. If pieces of potato are placed in water or strong sucrose solution, they either swell up or shrink. This is because they either gain or lose water.

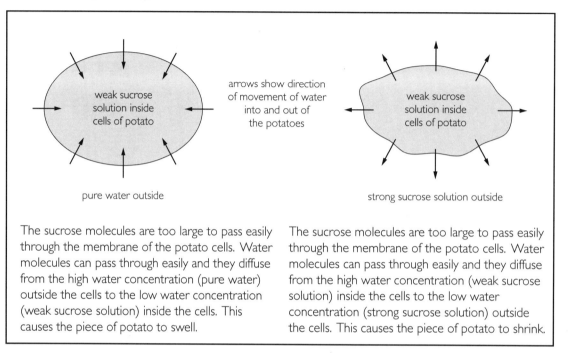

The sucrose molecules are too large to pass easily through the membrane of the potato cells. Water molecules can pass through easily and they diffuse from the high water concentration (pure water) outside the cells to the low water concentration (weak sucrose solution) inside the cells. This causes the piece of potato to swell.

The sucrose molecules are too large to pass easily through the membrane of the potato cells. Water molecules can pass through easily and they diffuse from the high water concentration (weak sucrose solution) inside the cells to the low water concentration (strong sucrose solution) outside the cells. This causes the piece of potato to shrink.

3. Osmosis

The potatoes shrink or swell up because the cells either lose water or gain water. This movement (diffusion) of water through the cell membrane is a special case of diffusion called **osmosis**.

Osmosis is the movement of water through a cell membrane from an area where it is in a high concentration to an area where it is in a low concentration.

4. Osmosis and animal cells

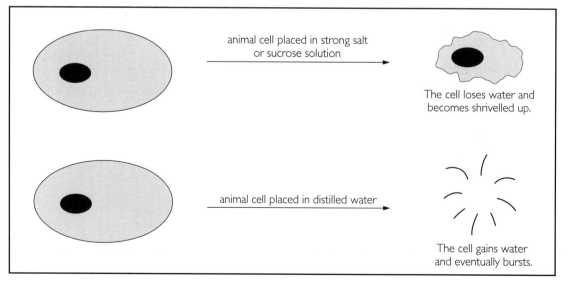

5. Osmosis and plant cells

Plant cells contain many substances dissolved in water to form a weak solution. During osmosis, water can either enter or leave the cell depending on the strength of the solution surrounding it.

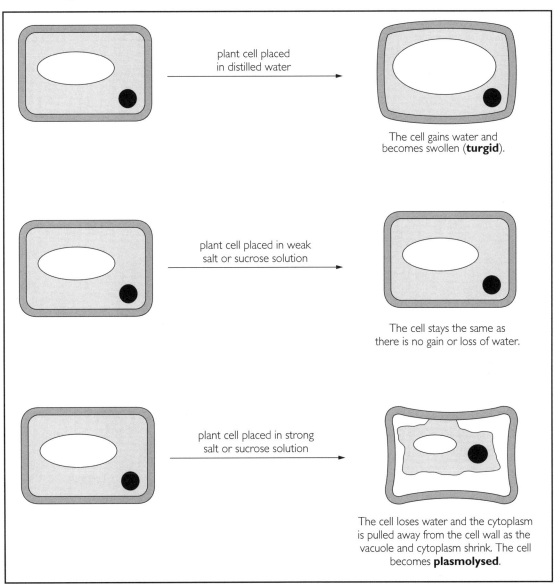

The cell membrane is described as being **selectively permeable** because it only allows smaller molecules (e.g. water) to pass through it and not larger ones (e.g. starch). Molecules which pass through the cell membrane do so because there is a high concentration on one side and a low concentration on the other. This is described as a **concentration gradient.**

INVESTIGATING CELL DIVISION

Cell division is an important process which increases the number of cells in an organism. It is also the way in which single-celled organisms reproduce. However, before a cell divides its nucleus must divide. The division of the nucleus is called **mitosis**.

Mitosis is important because it ensures that each new cell has a perfect copy of the instructions found in the nucleus which control the cell's development. These instructions are called **genes** and they are grouped together as **chromosomes**.

When a cell is ready to divide, long threads called chromosomes appear in the nucleus. These threads contain all the information necessary for the control of the cell and all the instructions necessary to build a whole new organism. Before a cell divides, a new set of chromosomes must be made so that the instructions can be passed on to the daughter cells.

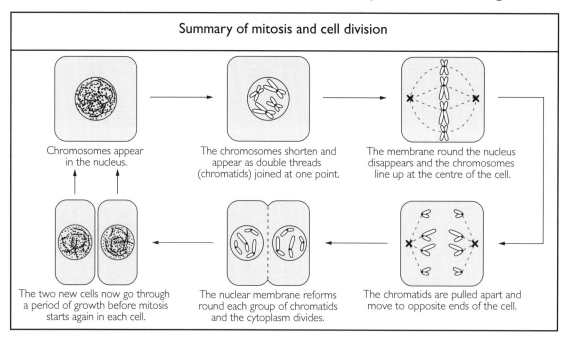

Summary of mitosis and cell division

Chromosomes appear in the nucleus.

The chromosomes shorten and appear as double threads (chromatids) joined at one point.

The membrane round the nucleus disappears and the chromosomes line up at the centre of the cell.

The two new cells now go through a period of growth before mitosis starts again in each cell.

The nuclear membrane reforms round each group of chromatids and the cytoplasm divides.

The chromatids are pulled apart and move to opposite ends of the cell.

INVESTIGATING ENZYMES

1. Cell reactions

A chemical reaction is where one molecule, or a group of molecules, changes in some way. Chemical reactions occur in cells all the time. One example is the changing of hydrogen peroxide into water and oxygen. We would write it this way:

hydrogen peroxide $\longrightarrow$ water + oxygen

There are two types of reaction:

(a) **breakdown reactions**: where one molecule breaks down into smaller molecules.

starch $\longrightarrow$ maltose

(b) **synthesis reactions**: where molecules join together to make a larger molecule.

glucose-1-phosphate $\longrightarrow$ starch

2. What are enzymes?

Enzymes are **catalysts**. Catalysts are chemicals which speed up reactions. Almost all cell reactions are speeded up, or helped, by enzymes.

The molecule that an enzyme works on is called the **substrate**.

The molecule that is produced is called the **product**.

starch $\xrightarrow{\text{amylase}}$ maltose
(substrate)   (enzyme)   (product)

glucose-1-phosphate $\xrightarrow{\text{potato phosphorylase}}$ starch
(substrate)   (enzyme)   (product)

3. More information about enzymes

(a) Enzymes are made from protein.

(b) They can be used over and over again. They are never used up in reactions.

(c) They are specific. This means that each enzyme can only react with one set of substrate molecules. For example, the enzyme catalase will only affect the breakdown of hydrogen peroxide into water and oxygen. It does not affect any other reaction.

(d) Enzymes are affected by temperature:

(i) They work slower at cold temperatures.

(ii) They work faster at warm temperatures.

(iii) The temperature they work best at is called the **optimum** temperature. The optimum temperature for most mammal enzymes is 37°C. Some plant enzymes have an optimum temperature around 20°C.

(iv) At high temperatures (over 50°C) many enzymes are denatured. This means that they are altered in shape and cannot work.

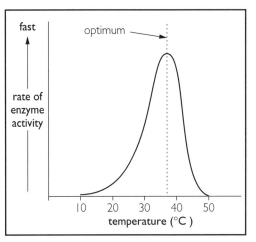

(e) Enzymes are affected by pH. The pH an enzyme works best at is called its optimum pH.

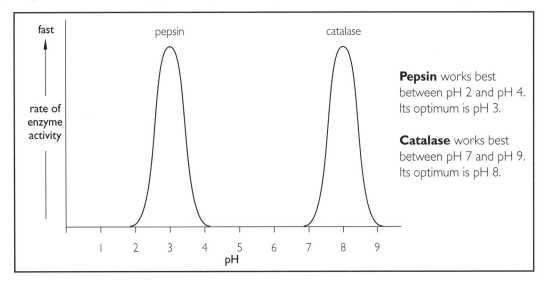

Pepsin works best between pH 2 and pH 4. Its optimum is pH 3.

Catalase works best between pH 7 and pH 9. Its optimum is pH 8.

4. Enzymes and cell chemistry

Almost all the reactions which happen inside an organism are controlled by enzymes. Without enzymes these reactions would go too slowly for life to exist. Enzymes are essential for life. Most processes in an organism consist of many reactions, each of which is catalysed by an enzyme. These processes are what we call **metabolism**. Some examples are given below:

(a) **photosynthesis**

(b) **respiration**

(c) **protein synthesis**

(d) **digestion**

INVESTIGATING AEROBIC RESPIRATION

Living things need energy to grow, to move and to reproduce. They obtain this energy from food. The energy in food is chemical energy. When food is broken down, it can be converted to another form of energy. For example:

chemical energy in food ⟶ movement (kinetic) energy

chemical energy in food ⟶ heat energy

1. Energy content of food

All foods contain energy, but some contain more than others. Fats and oils contain twice as much energy as proteins and carbohydrates.

fats and oils	38 kJ per gram
carbohydrates	17 kJ per gram
proteins	22 kJ per gram

Although carbohydrates contain less energy, it is easier to release the energy from them than from fats and proteins. Therefore the main energy supply for most organisms comes from carbohydrate in the form of glucose. The process which releases energy from food is **respiration**.

2. Aerobic respiration

When oxygen is used in respiration, it is described as **aerobic respiration**. What happens in cells is shown in the reaction below:

glucose + oxygen ⟶ carbon dioxide + water + *energy*

The carbon dioxide produced is released to the surroundings.

3. Uses of energy

The energy released by respiration is often in the form of heat energy. Mammals and birds use this heat energy to keep warm. Energy is also needed for movement and for most of the reactions that take place in cells.

4. Measuring respiration

During aerobic respiration, oxygen gas is used up and carbon dioxide gas is produced. A simple piece of apparatus can be used to show these gas changes during respiration. This piece of apparatus is called a respirometer.

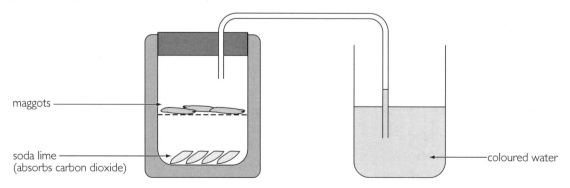

maggots

soda lime
(absorbs carbon dioxide)

coloured water

As the oxygen is used up by the maggots, the coloured water moves towards them up the glass tube. The carbon dioxide they breathe out is absorbed by the soda lime and so does not push the water back. We can place the maggots in different conditions (e.g. hot or cold) and compare the rate of movement of the coloured water. This is a measure of the rate of respiration.

UNIT FIVE: The Body in Action

MOVEMENT

Animals must be able to move in order to find food, and some have limbs that allow them to move easily.

For physical activity to take place animals require:

(a) support
(b) a means of movement
(c) energy
(d) co-ordination

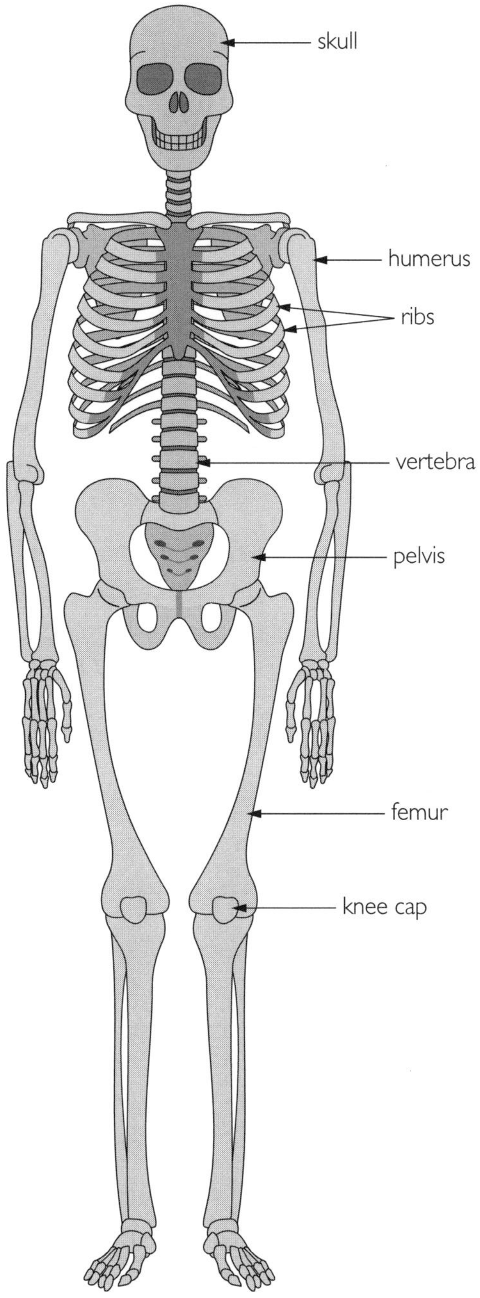

1. The human skeleton

The skeleton has a number of functions:

(a) it keeps our shape
(b) it supports our weight
(c) it protects vital organs such as the brain, heart, lungs and spinal cord
(d) it provides a framework for the attachment of muscles

2. The structure of bone

Bones are alive. They are made of living cells. These cells are made of **flexible fibres** and are surrounded by **hard minerals**.

The living cells give bones flexibility.

The minerals give bones strength and hardness.

(diagram labels: skull, humerus, ribs, vertebra, pelvis, femur, knee cap)

3. Joints

A joint is a place where two or more bones meet (e.g. elbow or shoulder).

Different joints in the body allow different types of movement.

Type of joint	Types of movement possible	Examples
ball and socket	in all directions	shoulder and hip
hinge joint	in one plane (like a hinge)	knee and elbow

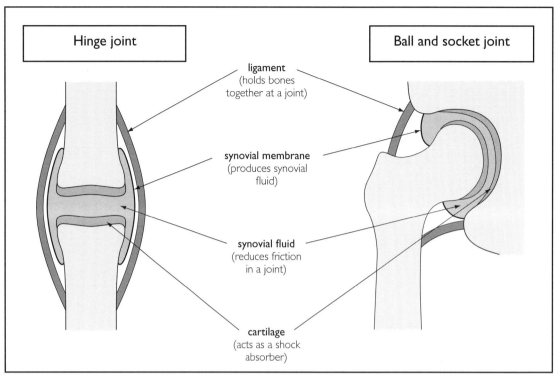

A joint is an efficient structure because friction and shock are reduced by the smooth **cartilage** and the oily, slippery **synovial fluid**. **Ligaments** are strong fibres which hold bones together at joints. They are elastic to allow the bones to move.

4. Muscles and movement

To permit movement the entire skeleton is covered in muscle. A muscle works by pulling on a bone. To do this the muscle has to contract (shorten).

Muscles are attached to bones by **tendons**.

Tendons are very strong and do not stretch so that the muscle can pull on the bone effectively.

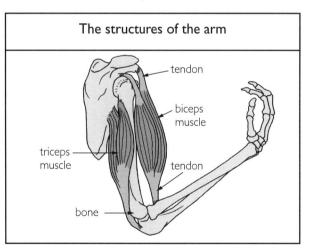

The muscles at a joint always work in pairs. One muscle makes the joint bend while the other straightens it.

To bend the arm at the elbow, the muscle at the front of the upper arm (the biceps) contracts. To straighten the arm, the muscle at the back of the upper arm (the triceps) contracts.

Muscles work in pairs – when one of the pair is contracted, the other is relaxed.

5. Sports injuries

If you get involved in a strenuous activity such as sport, it is possible to injure your joints, muscles and tendons. Some parts of the body are more likely to be injured than others. The most common injury is to the knee and the least common is to the head and neck. Sports injuries occur because of the sudden changes of movement and the knocks that can happen.

THE NEED FOR ENERGY

Your body needs energy to take part in sport or any other activity that involves movement.

Different foods contain different amounts of energy. To release the energy in food, it must be combined with oxygen in the body. During this process, carbon dioxide is produced as a waste product.

If a person's energy input (i.e. food intake) is higher than their energy output then their body stores this extra energy in the form of fat. If a person's energy output is higher than their energy input, then they will lose weight.

1. The structure of lungs

The oxygen you need to release energy from food is obtained by breathing in (inhaling). The carbon dioxide produced as a waste product is removed by breathing out (exhaling).

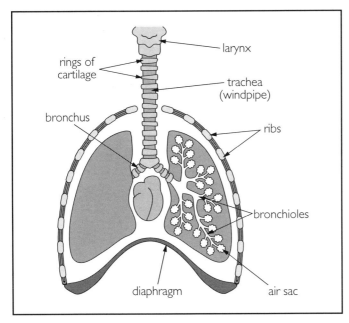

Air comes in at the mouth and passes down the **trachea**. On the way, it passes through the larynx (voice box). The trachea is held open by **rings of cartilage**. The air then passes down a **bronchus**, which divides into many tiny tubes called **bronchioles**. The bronchioles end in **air sacs**.

2. Gas exchange in the air sacs

The air sacs are lined with moisture. Oxygen, in the breathed-in (inhaled) air, dissolves in this moisture and diffuses into the blood. Carbon dioxide diffuses in the opposite direction from the capillary into the air sac.

Whenever gases are exchanged, three conditions are necessary if the gases are to be exchanged efficiently. These are:

(a) **large surface** – there are many tiny air sacs

(b) **thin surface** – the air sac and capillary are only one cell thick

(c) **moist surface** – film of water inside the air sac

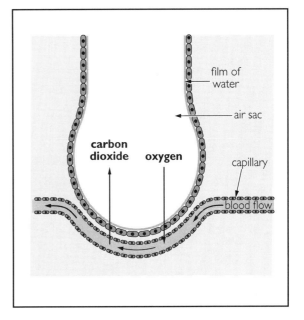

3. Cleaning inhaled air

The air you breathe in often contains dust and germs which must be removed from the lungs. The air entering the lungs is cleaned by special cells lining the air tubes. These cells have small hair-like extensions, called **cilia**, which beat in waves. A slippery liquid, called mucus, is also made by these cells. This mucus traps the dust and germs. The cilia beat and move the mucus towards the mouth. In this way, dust and germs are carried up to the mouth and then swallowed.

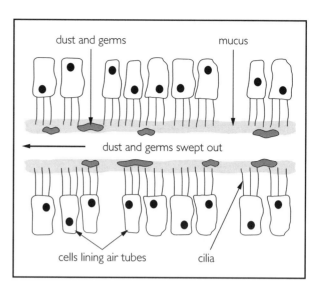

4. Breathing movements

When we breathe, our chest moves in and out like a pair of bellows. The ribs move up and out, and down and in. At the same time, the **diaphragm** also moves up and down.

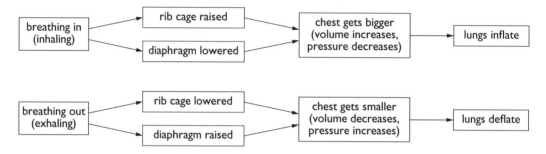

5. Heart structure

Once oxygen enters the body, it has to be carried to all the cells of the body. It is carried by blood in the blood vessels. The heart pumps the blood around the body.

The power required by the heart to pump blood around the body is produced by muscles in the heart wall.

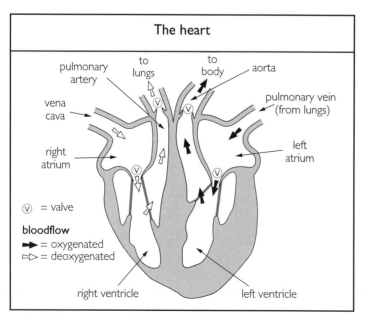

The function of the **heart valves** is to keep blood flowing in one direction and to stop backflow.

The wall of the **left ventricle** is thicker than the wall of the **right ventricle** because it has to pump blood all around the body. The right ventricle only pumps blood to the lungs.

The heart gets its own blood supply from the **coronary arteries** which run over its surface.

The flow chart below shows the path taken by blood on its way through the heart to the lungs, back to the heart and out to the body.

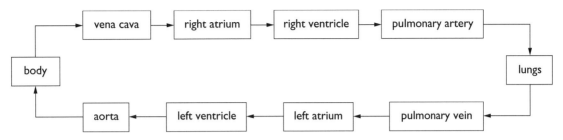

6. Blood vessels

Blood is carried all around the body in blood vessels. Blood leaves the heart and is carried in **arteries**. The arteries branch into tiny tubes called **capillaries**. The capillaries then join up to form **veins** which carry blood back to the heart.

Each time the heart beats blood is pushed along the arteries. This can be felt when you take your **pulse**.

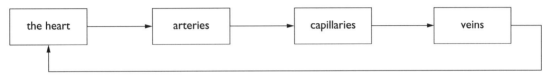

As blood flows through the capillaries, oxygen diffuses from the capillaries into the body cells. In exchange, carbon dioxide diffuses from the body cells into the capillaries. As with gas exchange in the air sacs, the same three conditions are required for gas exchange in the capillaries. These are:

(a) large surface – many capillaries
(b) thin surface   – capillaries are only one cell thick
(c) moist surface – body cells are all bathed in a fluid

7. Blood

Blood is made up of cells carried in a liquid called **plasma**.

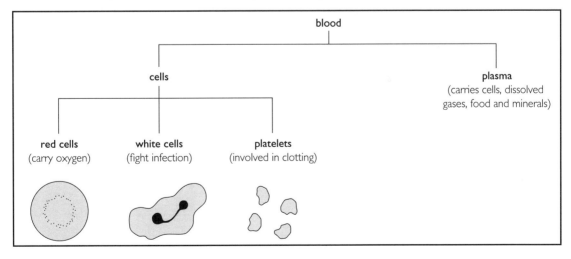

Red cells carry oxygen round the body. They contain the chemical **haemoglobin**. Haemoglobin combines with oxygen to form oxyhaemoglobin. In the capillaries, the oxygen is released from the haemoglobin and diffuses into the body cells.

CO-ORDINATION

Our nervous system controls every action we make. The sense organs respond to information from our surroundings (e.g. sound and light) and send messages to our brain and spinal cord. The brain and spinal cord sort out this information and send instructions to the body, which then responds.

1. The eye

The eye is the sense organ which detects light. Having two eyes allows us to judge distance. Each eye sees a slightly different view. The brain puts these two views together to form a three-dimensional view which helps in the judgement of distances. This is called **binocular vision**.

The eye	cornea	bends the light as it enters the eye so that it can be focussed on the retina
	iris	changes size of the pupil in different light intensities
	pupil	allows light to enter the eye
	lens	focuses light on the retina
	retina	contains the light-sensitive cells
	optic nerve	carries messages from the light-sensitive cells to the brain

2. The ear

The ear is the sense organ used to detect sound. Our judgement of where a sound has come from is made more accurate by having two ears.

The ear	ear drum	vibrates when sound waves reach it
	middle ear bones	carry the vibrations from the ear drum to the cochlea
	cochlea	contains cells which are sensitive to sound vibrations
	auditory nerve	carries messages from the vibration-sensitive cells to the brain

3. Balance

The **semicircular canals** help us to keep our balance. They are three tubes each at right angles to each other. When the head moves, cells in the walls of the canals pick up the movement of fluid in the canals and send messages to the brain.

4. The nervous system

The nervous system controls the body. It consists of the **brain, spinal cord** and **nerves**.

Nerves are made up of many nerve cells. Some nerve cells are stretched out into long, thin fibres that can be over one metre long. Nerve impulses travel along nerve cell fibres in one direction. There are three types of nerve cells which are involved in the flow of information. These are shown in the diagram below.

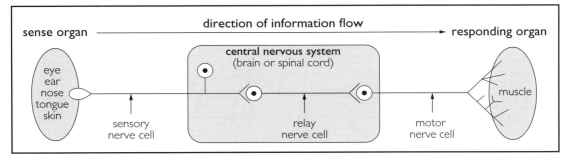

A stimulus (e.g. heat) is detected by the sense organ and a nerve impulse is sent along the sensory nerve cell to the central nervous system. The central nervous system works out the best response and sends an impulse along the motor nerve cell to the muscle. The muscle responds by contracting or relaxing.

5. A reflex action

A reflex action is a rapid, automatic response to a stimulus which is usually dangerous. It protects the body by allowing it to react quickly. A reflex action involves a flow of information into and out of the spinal cord, only involving the brain after the action has taken place. This is called a **reflex arc** and is shown in the diagram below.

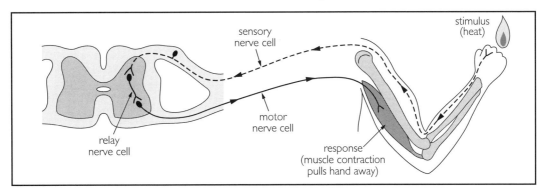

6. The brain

The brain is at the top of the spinal cord and is protected by the skull.

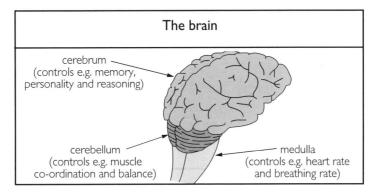

CHANGING LEVELS OF PERFORMANCE

1. Exercise and fatigue

When we run fast, our muscles use up lots of glucose in producing energy. Sometimes not enough oxygen gets to the muscles, so respiration without oxygen (**anaerobic respiration**) takes place. Instead of being broken down to carbon dioxide and water, glucose is broken down into a chemical called **lactic acid**. Lactic acid builds up in the muscles and causes soreness and fatigue.

aerobic respiration:	glucose + oxygen ⟶ carbon dioxide + water + *energy*
anaerobic respiration:	glucose ⟶ lactic acid + *energy*

At the end of the exercise, we get rid of the lactic acid by breathing rapidly to take in more oxygen. The lactic acid then breaks down to carbon dioxide and water. The volume of oxygen needed to breathe in to break down the lactic acid is called the **oxygen debt**.

2. The effects of training

During exercise, the pulse and breathing rates increase. This means that the heart is beating faster to carry more glucose and oxygen to the contracting muscles. The **recovery time** is the time taken for the pulse and breathing rate to return to normal after the exercise is over.

Training has the following effects on the body:

(a) it increases heart volume and the volume of blood sent out during each beat, causing a lower resting pulse rate;
(b) the efficiency of gas exchange in the lungs is improved;
(c) it produces a faster recovery time as lactic acid is removed more quickly;
(d) it improves circulation to muscles.

This training effect is shown in the diagram below.

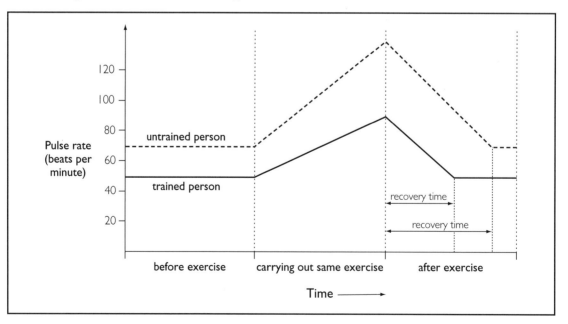

UNIT SIX: Inheritance

VARIATION

What is a species?

A species is a group of living things that are so similar to each other that:

(a) they are able to interbreed and produce offspring

(b) the offspring are fertile (able to produce offspring of their own)

No two members of a species are exactly alike. Differences exist between all individuals. In other words, variation occurs between individuals.

There are two types of variation:

(1) **continuous variation**   (2) **discontinuous variation**

1. Continuous variation

This type of variation contains no distinct groups of individuals and any differences between individuals can be measured. Within a large group, any characteristic will vary from one extreme to another, e.g. from very small to very tall.

A large group can be surveyed for a particular characteristic which is an example of continuous variation. The results can then be displayed as a graph. The shape of the graph may be like the two drawn below.

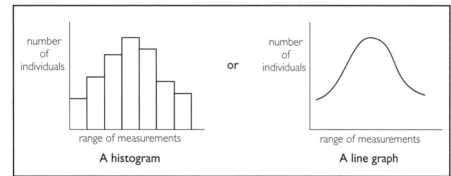

A histogram   or   A line graph

Typical examples of characteristics which show continuous variation are pulse rate (beats per minute), height and weight.

2. Discontinuous variation

In this type of variation, individuals can be divided into two or more distinct groups.

A survey of a large group may produce the following types of graphs:

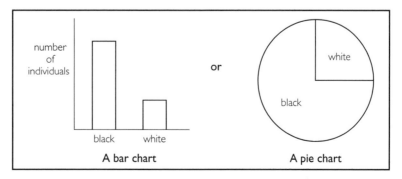

A bar chart   or   A pie chart

WHAT IS INHERITANCE?

All characteristics (e.g. hair colour, blood group, colour of flowers) are determined by genetic information. This information is carried on the chromosomes found in the nucleus of every cell.

Each parent passes some genetic information to its offspring.

1. Inherited characteristics

Characteristics can exist in different forms, for example:

Organism	Characteristic	Possible form (phenotype)
human	eye colour	blue, brown, green, grey
	blood group	A, B, O, AB
fruit-fly	wing length	long, short
	eye colour	red, white
pea plant	seed shape	round, wrinkled
	seed colour	green, yellow

The **phenotype** is the appearance or nature of the organism with respect to its genes.

2. Passing on characteristics

If an organism with a particular phenotype is crossed (mated) with another which shows the same phenotype, it can produce offspring which all show the same phenotype. If only that phenotype, and no other, appears in all the subsequent generations, the original parent organisms are described as **true breeding**.

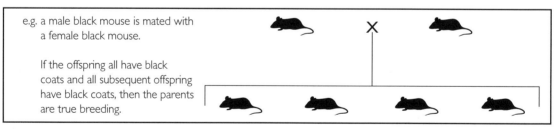

e.g. a male black mouse is mated with a female black mouse.

If the offspring all have black coats and all subsequent offspring have black coats, then the parents are true breeding.

If a true breeding black mouse is crossed with a true breeding brown mouse the offspring are all black.

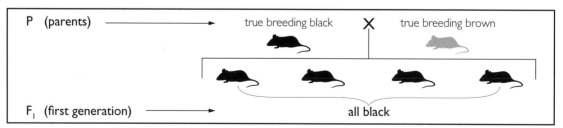

P (parents) ——————→ true breeding black X true breeding brown

F₁ (first generation) ——————→ all black

All the offspring are black because the black gene is **dominant** to the brown gene. The brown gene is **recessive** to the black gene. The brown gene only influences the phenotype when two are present.

If two of the F$_1$ offspring are crossed with each other then the next generation, the F$_2$ generation, will have some black and some brown haired mice. There will, however, always be more black mice. If large numbers of offspring are produced, the ratio of black (dominant) to brown (recessive) will be approximately 3:1.

3. Chromosome sets and genes

The sex cells (gametes) contain only one set of chromosomes. When fertilisation takes place, the chromosome set of the egg joins with the chromosome set of the sperm. The nucleus of the fertilised egg (zygote) now contains two matching sets of chromosomes. The zygote divides to produce all the other cells of the body. This means that every cell has the same two sets of chromosomes.

When the two sets of chromosomes are examined, they can be arranged in pairs – one of the pair will have come from the mother and the other from the father.

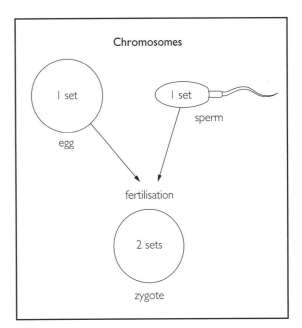

Each chromosome carries information on many tiny units called **genes**. It is these genes that determine the characteristics of an organism.

All characteristics are determined by genes. The gene for each characteristic exists in two or more forms (**alleles**). One form is usually dominant and the other is recessive. One example in humans is tongue rolling. There are two tongue rolling alleles. One allele allows humans to roll their tongues. The other allele does not. Depending on which combination of these alleles your cells contain, you either can or cannot roll your tongue. The tongue rolling allele is dominant to the non-rolling allele.

Phenotype of person	Tongue roller	Tongue roller	Non-tongue roller
Alleles contained in body cells	tongue rolling allele tongue rolling allele	tongue rolling allele non-rolling allele	non-rolling allele non-rolling allele

The diagram below shows how the coat colour alleles are passed on when true breeding mice are crossed.

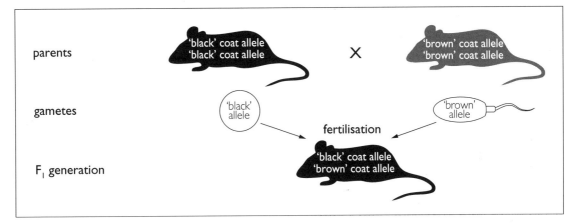

4. The monohybrid cross

The two forms of a particular gene (allele) can be represented by letters. The dominant allele is always represented by a capital letter and the recessive allele by a small letter. Tallness in pea plants is dominant to dwarfness. These alleles are represented as follows:

T = tallness   **t = dwarfness**

Each characteristic of an organism is determined by two alleles. The two alleles present in an organism are known as its **genotype**.

A tall pea plant has the genotype TT or Tt.

A dwarf pea plant has the genotype tt.

If the two alleles are the same, (TT or tt), the genotype is described as **homozygous**.

If the two alleles are different (Tt), the genotype is described as **heterozygous**.

Phenotype	Genotype	Description of genotype
tall	TT	homozygous dominant
tall	Tt	heterozygous
dwarf	tt	homozygous recessive

The simplest genetic cross involves one characteristic and is called a **monohybrid cross**.

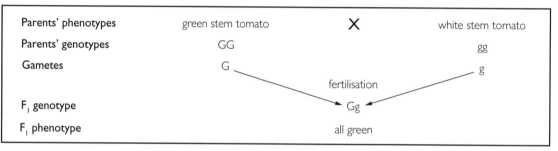

Parents' phenotypes	green stem tomato	**X**	white stem tomato
Parents' genotypes	GG		gg
Gametes	G		g
		fertilisation	
F_1 genotype		Gg	
F_1 phenotype		all green	

The next step might involve crossing two individuals from the F_1 generation.

F_1 phenotype	green stem tomato	**X**	green stem tomato
F_1 genotype	Gg		Gg
Gametes	G and g (in equal numbers)		G and g (in equal numbers)

A grid is then used to show the possible ways in which these two sets of gametes could combine during fertilisation.

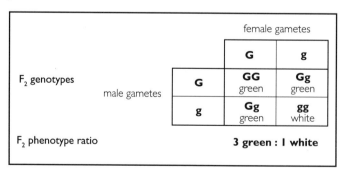

F_2 genotypes

		female gametes	
		G	**g**
male gametes **G**		**GG** green	**Gg** green
g		**Gg** green	**gg** white

F_2 phenotype ratio   **3 green : 1 white**

An approximate 3:1 ratio is only likely to occur when large numbers of offspring are produced. This is because the fusion of gametes at fertilisation is random and is a matter of chance (like tossing a coin). If a coin is tossed 10 times you could expect 5 heads and 5 tails but in reality that may not happen.

5. Sex determination

In many organisms sex is determined by a pair of chromosomes, the **sex chromosomes**. They are called the **X and Y chromosomes**.

In humans a female has the genotype XX and a male has the genotype XY.

The diagram opposite shows how sex is inherited.

The ratio of girls to boys is 1:1

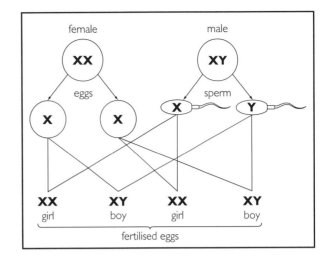

GENETICS AND SOCIETY

1. Selective breeding

For centuries, animal and plant breeders have tried to improve their stock and their crops (e.g. dairy farmers want to have cows which produce large quantities of milk). Improved characteristics can be obtained by selective breeding. Breeders select and breed those varieties of animals and plants with characteristics that are useful. Selective breeding has resulted in, for example:

(a) Aberdeen Angus cattle bred for beef production
(b) sheep bred to produce better wool
(c) poultry bred to grow more quickly
(d) cereals bred to be more resistant to disease

2. Mutations

Almost 1% of all babies are born with some sort of change to their chromosomes. These changes are called mutations. **Down's Syndrome**, for example, is caused by a chromosome mutation. Children with Down's Syndrome have an extra chromosome (47 instead of 46).

Mutations occur naturally, but are rare. Radiation, such as X-rays and fallout from atomic bombs, can increase mutation rate. Some chemicals can also cause mutations.

Not all mutations are harmful. Some can be useful. Extra chromosomes in spinach and sugar beet, for example, make these plants grow stronger.

3. Amniocentesis

A technique called amniocentesis can be used to remove cells from the womb so that chromosome changes can be detected in an embryo.

A sample of amniotic fluid can be removed using a special syringe. The fluid contains cells from the baby's skin. The cells can be grown in the laboratory and then examined to see if there are any defects in the chromosomes. The fluid can also be tested to see if it contains certain chemicals which may indicate a chromosome abnormality.

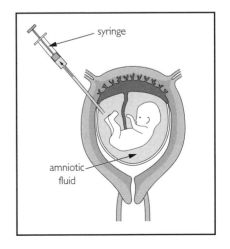

UNIT SEVEN: Biotechnology

LIVING FACTORIES

Biotechnology is the use of living cells to convert raw materials into useful substances. The living cells may come from plants, animals or micro-organisms.

1. Fermentation

Yeast is a living organism. It is a **single-celled fungus** which can feed and grow on sugar. Yeast can respire anaerobically. This means that it breaks down sugars (e.g. glucose) to release energy without using oxygen. As it does this, it also produces carbon dioxide and ethanol (alcohol).

This process is called fermentation and is summarised in the word equation below.

$$\text{glucose} \longrightarrow \text{carbon dioxide + ethanol + } \textit{energy}$$

Yeast is important in baking because the carbon dioxide produced makes the bread rise. Baking the bread finally kills the yeast and cooks the dough. Alcohol is the useful product of fermentation used in brewing and wine making.

2. Batch processing

Allowing yeast to ferment sugar can be done on a large scale. Batch processing is a technique used by commercial brewers. A large reactor vessel (a **fermenter**) is filled with the necessary raw materials and given the best conditions to promote fermentation.

After the fermenter has been set up, the system is closed and left until fermentation is complete. Then the products can be collected and purified.

Yeast grows best in warm conditions with an adequate supply of glucose and oxygen and a pH of 7. An absence of other micro-organisms (sterile conditions) is essential as these may slow down the process or produce other, unwanted, substances.

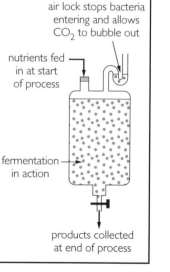

air lock stops bacteria entering and allows CO_2 to bubble out

nutrients fed in at start of process

fermentation in action

products collected at end of process

3. The malting of beer

To make beer, brewers use barley as food for yeast. However, barley grains contain starch and not the simple sugar that yeast can feed on. The barley must be allowed to germinate in moist, warm conditions in a process called **malting**. During this time, enzymes present in the barley break down the starch into the sugar maltose on which the yeast can feed.

$$\text{starch} \xrightarrow{\text{enzymes in barley grains}} \text{maltose} \xrightarrow{\text{yeast}} \text{carbon dioxide + ethanol + } \textit{energy}$$

4. Other fermentation processes

Fresh milk contains a sugar called **lactose**. When bacteria feed on this sugar, they break it down in a fermentation process and produce **lactic acid**. This acid makes the milk taste sour. The pH of the milk becomes more and more acidic as more lactose is fermented.

Yoghurt and cheese are produced by adding particular types of bacteria to milk.

PROBLEMS AND PROFIT WITH WASTE

Microbes (micro-organisms) are tiny living things that can only be seen using a microscope. They include bacteria, viruses and some fungi. Microbes can be useful, but they can also be harmful.

1. Working with microbes

Certain precautions have to be taken when working with microbes to ensure unwanted microbes are not able to grow and cause disease.

Safe handling of microbes	
(a) Wash hands and laboratory bench.	(c) Never open dishes containing microbes.
(b) Always use sterile equipment.	(d) Always dispose of dishes containing microbes by using high temperatures.

Contamination is the presence of unwanted, possibly harmful microbes. Many manufacturing processes (e.g. brewing) have to include special precautions to ensure that all equipment is clean and sterile. After every batch of beer is brewed the equipment is sterilised by using steam heat and chemicals. This is to destroy resistant fungi and bacteria which other methods of sterilisation do not kill. For example, boiling does not kill some fungal and bacterial spores.

2. Microbes and decay

After a plant or animal has died, its tissues decay. Fungi and bacteria cause decay. They use the dead material as their food source to obtain energy and building materials to stay alive and grow. These microbes, called **decomposers**, can only use organic (natural) substances. Substances such as plastic do not decay easily.

3. The treatment of sewage

Untreated sewage contains faeces, detergents, food fragments and bacteria which can cause great damage if dumped into a river. Some of these effects are shown below.

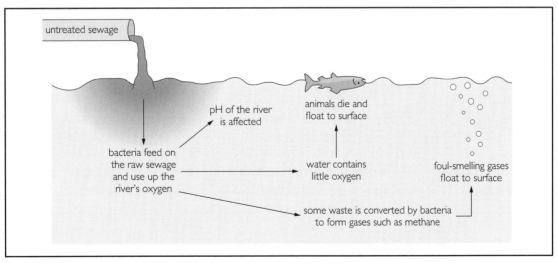

Some of the microbes in untreated sewage can cause diseases such as **dysentery**, **typhoid**, **cholera** and food poisoning.

The treatment of sewage involves the conversion of harmful materials to harmless products by the use of microbes.

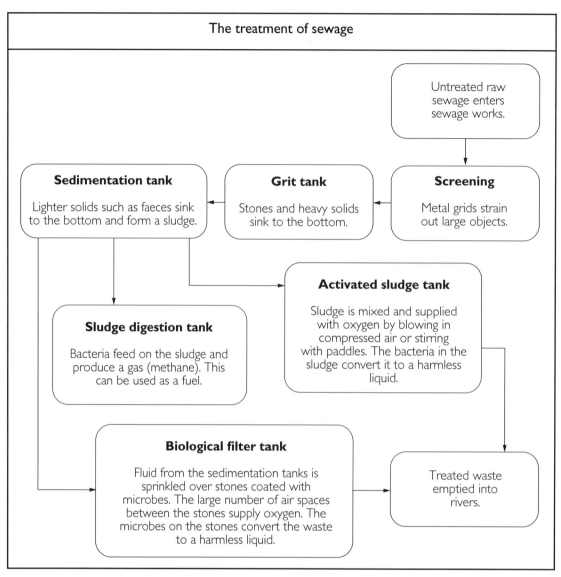

Many different types of microbe are used in sewage treatment to ensure the complete breakdown of all the different substances present in the sewage. Complete breakdown is only possible when oxygen is present for aerobic respiration. Without oxygen, sewage is only partially broken down, leaving some harmful products.

4. Upgrading waste

Many manufacturing processes produce organic waste products. These can be fed to microbes which convert them to products which are useful to people and other animals. The advantage is that unwanted waste products can be converted to products with a high energy or protein value. Consequently, they have a higher economic value than the original waste.

Type of waste	Useful product	Use made of product
manure	biogas	fuel
fruit pulp	food rich in protein	animal feed

5. Fuels from microbes

When microbes grow on fresh manure, they produce **methane** gas. When yeast feeds on sugar, it produces **alcohol**. Both the methane and the alcohol can be used as fuels. These two fuels are described as **renewable** energy sources whereas fossil fuels (coal, oil and gas) are **non-renewable** energy sources. There are advantages to using renewable energy sources rather than fossil fuels. They are less harmful to the environment and can always be replaced.

6. Other uses of microbes

Microbes can reproduce very rapidly by dividing into two. Given food, water and heat, one bacterium can result in many thousands of bacteria within a few hours. Industry makes use of fast-growing bacteria to produce protein-rich foods, as a high percentage of a bacterium is protein.

Bacteria can be grown, harvested and dried to form a protein-rich powder called single-celled protein which is used as animal feed.

Some fungi produce a protein, called mycoprotein, which can be processed to produce meat-like products for cooking.

7. The carbon cycle

Decay is important in nature to ensure that minerals locked up in dead animals and plants are recycled. Both the nitrogen and carbon cycle involve bacteria. The carbon cycle involves the recycling of carbon.

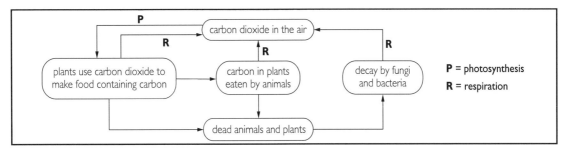

REPROGRAMMING MICROBES

1. Genetic engineering

Genetic engineering is a technique which involves taking a gene from one organism and transferring it into another. The other organism then makes a new chemical under the instruction of the transferred gene. As bacteria reproduce rapidly and are easy to grow, they are often used in genetic engineering. In this way, large quantities of a chemical, such as **insulin**, can be made.

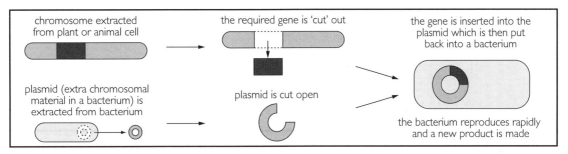

2. Products of genetic engineering

Insulin is a hormone which controls blood sugar concentrations. It is produced by the pancreas. People who suffer from diabetes cannot make their own insulin. Until recently, diabetics used sheep and pig insulin but some people are allergic to them as they are not identical to human insulin. Genetic engineering can reprogramme bacteria to produce large volumes of insulin identical to human insulin. The gene which makes insulin can be cut from a human chromosome and inserted into a bacterial **plasmid**. The rapidly-dividing bacteria produce the insulin which can be collected and purified. Genetic engineering and selective breeding both involve altering the genotype of an organism. Genetic engineering is faster and produces the organism with the new genotype immediately. Selective breeding is a long process which does not always produce the organism required.

3. Antibiotics

Other important products of genetic engineering are **antibiotics**, which can kill bacteria. The best known antibiotic is penicillin, which is produced by a fungus. There are many other antibiotics such as streptomycin and erythromycin. A single antibiotic is not always effective against all bacteria, as many bacteria become resistant to a particular antibiotic. So new antibiotics are constantly being developed. Antibiotics have no effect on viruses.

4. Biological detergents

Biological detergents contain enzymes produced by bacteria. These are able to break down difficult protein stains such as those caused by grass, blood and egg. Biological detergents are effective at removing stains at low temperatures (40°C) which non-biological detergents would not remove. Stain removal at such low temperatures prevents damage being done to fabrics and saves on fuel costs.

5. Immobilisation

Immobilisation is a technique that fixes enzymes onto substances such as jelly or glass beads. In this way they can be used again and again without having to separate them continually from the products of their action. Whole cells, such as yeast, can also be immobilised in this way.

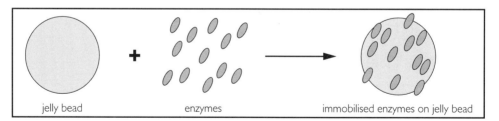

jelly bead   enzymes   immobilised enzymes on jelly bead

6. Continuous flow processing

Immobilised enzymes are placed in a fermenter. Nutrients can be continually fed in and the end products continuously collected and purified. This is known as continuous flow processing.

This method increases productivity and reduces costs compared with batch processing as used in brewing.

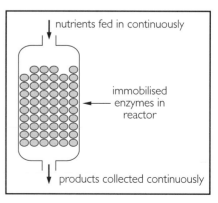

nutrients fed in continuously

immobilised enzymes in reactor

products collected continuously